I WONDER ABOUT

PLANTS

Jean Watson

D1133918

Pictures by Ann Blockley

LITTLE LIONS

I wonder why seeds
    are so full of surprises,
And grow into
    so many colours and sizes.

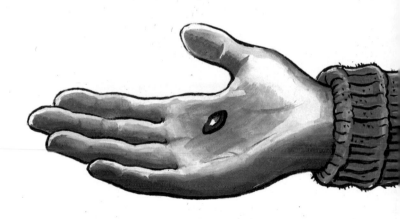

I wonder why
   one little seed can become,
A plant, or a tree,
   like an apple or plum.

I wonder why trees
    wear no leaves when it's cold,
Then put on, in summer,
    their leafiest clothes.

I wonder why plants
   have so many roots,
Perhaps they are needed
   to grow all the shoots.

I wonder why leaves
    are so good to chew,
For grubs and slugs
    and caterpillars, too.

I wonder why plants
have different smells
Their colours and shapes
are different, as well.

But when I grow older
  I won't only wonder,
I'll listen and learn
  and start to find out;
For I'm glad that this beautiful
  world which God made
Is so full of things
  to wonder about.

Copyright © 1983 Lion Publishing
Published by
Lion Publishing plc
Icknield Way, Tring, Herts, England
ISBN 0 85648 459 8
Lion Publishing Corporation
772 Airport Boulevard, Ann Arbor, Michigan 48106, USA
ISBN 0 85648 459 8
Albatross Books
PO Box 320, Sutherland, NSW 2232, Australia
ISBN 0 86760 247 3

First edition 1983
Reprinted 1983

Printed by Artes Gráficas Toledo, S.A. Spain

D. L. TO: 686 -1983